The Lewis and Clark Expedition: Crossing the Rocky Mountains

Building the Transcontinental Railroad: Blasting Through the Sierra Nevadas

Two Historical Fiction Stories About Westward Expansion

by Stacia Deutsch and Rhody Cohon
illustrated by Helen Pavlac

Table of Contents

HISTORICAL FICTION

What is historical fiction?

Historical fiction stories take place in the past. Historical fiction stories have characters, settings, and events based on historical facts. The characters can be based on real people or made up. The dialogue is made up. But the information about the time period must be authentic, or factually accurate. The stories explore a conflict, or problem, that a character has with himself, with other characters, or with nature.

What is the purpose of historical fiction?

Historical fiction blends history and fiction into stories that could have actually happened. It adds a human element to history. Readers can learn about the time period: how people lived, what they owned, and even what they ate and wore. Readers can also see how people's problems and feelings have not changed much over time. In addition, historical fiction entertains us as we "escape" into adventures from the past.

How do you read historical fiction?

The title gives you a clue about an important time, place, character, or situation. As you read, note how the characters' lives are the same as and different from people's lives today. Note the main characters' thoughts, feelings, and actions. How do they change from the beginning of the story to the end? Ask yourself, *What moves this character to take action? What can I learn today from his or her struggles long ago?*

Features of Historical Fiction

The characters lived or could have lived in the time and place portrayed.

The story takes place in an authentic historical setting.

The events did occur or could have occurred in the setting.

The dialogue is made up but may be based on letters, a diary, or a report.

At least one character deals with a conflict (self, others, or nature).

The story is told from a first-person or third-person point of view.

Who tells the story in historical fiction?

Authors usually write historical fiction in one of two ways. In the first-person point of view, one of the characters tells the story as it happens to him or her, using words such as **I**, **me**, **my**, **mine**, **we**, **us**, and **our**. In the third-person point of view, a narrator tells the story and refers to the characters using words such as **he**, **him**, and **his**; **she**, **her**, and **hers**; and **their**. The narrator may also refer to the characters by name, for example, "Patrick was proud to be part of the journey."

TOOLS FOR READERS AND WRITERS

Alliteration

Alliteration is the repetition of the same beginning sound in words used in a sentence or phrase. One example is "Peter Piper picked a peck of pickled peppers." Alliteration is also the broader umbrella for consonance and assonance. Consonance is the repetition of the same consonant sound not at the beginning of each word, as in "yellow bells are mellow." Assonance is the repetition of the same vowel sound not at the beginning of each word, as in "Brave waifs live on whey." Alliteration gives writing a poetic, rhythmic quality, and it can also emphasize an action or a character's condition.

Homonyms

Homonyms are words that are spelled and pronounced the same but have different meanings, such as **skate** (*verb*—to glide on ice) and **skate** (*noun*—a fish). Some homonyms may have the same origin, such as **mouth** (*noun*—of an animal) and **mouth** (*noun*—of a river). Homonyms can be confusing, so read carefully to know which meaning the author intends.

Text Structure and Organization

Authors put words together in several ways called text structures or patterns. These text structures include cause and effect, compare and contrast/problem and solution (very similar and use the same key words), steps in a process or sequence of events, and description. In many cases, authors use key words and phrases that help readers determine the text structure being used.

About Westward Expansion

Louisiana Purchase

President Thomas Jefferson acquired the territory of Louisiana from France in 1803. This event, known as the Louisiana Purchase, doubled the size of the United States. Jefferson wanted to explore the new land to see if there was an all-water route between the central states and the Pacific Ocean.

Captains Meriwether Lewis and William Clark were chosen to lead the "Corps of Discovery" from St. Louis, Missouri, westward. During the spring and summer of 1804, the Corps of three dozen explorers crossed the Great Plains, mapping their route and collecting information about wildlife and plants. Seven of the men, including Sergeant Patrick Gass, kept diaries of their observations.

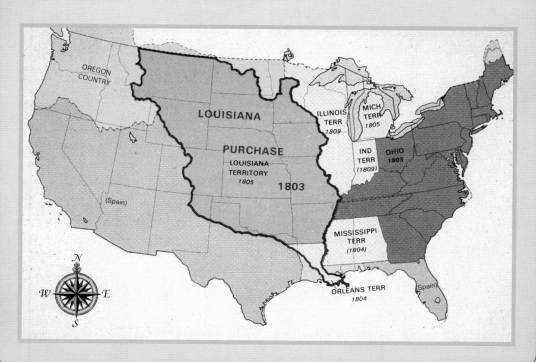

The Corps of Discovery stayed with the Mandan in North Dakota during their first winter. There they hired Toussaint Charbonneau, a French trapper, and Sacagawea, his Native American wife, as translators. When winter ended, they continued their journey, accompanied by Charbonneau, Sacagawea, and the couple's newborn baby boy. In May 1805, the travelers spied the Rocky Mountains. To cross them, they obtained horses from the Shoshone, whose chief was Sacagawea's brother. It rained and snowed during the difficult climb. By September, food was so scarce that the Corps was forced to eat some of the horses. Once the group made it over the Rockies, they were able to regain their strength at a Nez Perce tribal village. They finally reached the Pacific Ocean on December 3, 1805.

The return trip was less difficult. The explorers arrived back in St. Louis on September 23, 1806, after having traveled over 7,000 miles (11,265 kilometers). They had opened the way west for other travelers.

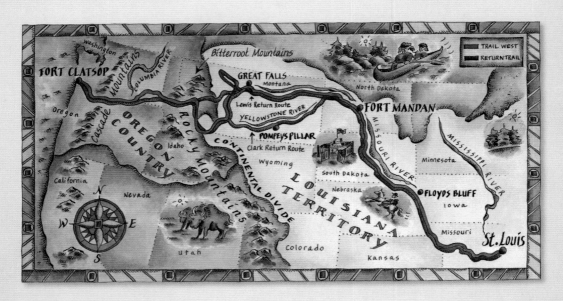

Transcontinental Railroad

In the early 1800s, settlers began to move west across the Northern Great Plains. This swell of people traveling westward intensified when gold was discovered in California in 1849. From that time forward, railroad engineers looked into the possibility of a single train line extending all the way west from the Missouri River. In 1862, Congress and President Lincoln signed the Pacific Railroad Bill into law. This document stated that the Central Pacific Railroad,

building from the west, and the Union Pacific Railroad, building from the east, were to meet.

It was hard going from California, where crews had to tunnel through parts of the Sierra Nevada Mountains. Many lives were lost; using pickaxes and black powder to make the necessary tunnels was slow work.

Railroad bosses managed to find workers who never gave up. Many of them were Chinese immigrants, who, despite their hard work, were treated differently than other workers. They received lower wages and were in separate living quarters.

A new, powerful explosive called nitroglycerin enabled the workers to blast through the mountains in 1867. Finally, on May 10, 1869, both railroads joined tracks at Promontory Point, Utah, making travel from east to west a reality.

The Lewis and Clark Expedition:
Crossing the Rocky Mountains

This oil painting of Sacagawea with Lewis and Clark is by N. C. Wyeth, a noted American artist and illustrator in the first half of the twentieth century.

"Hold up!" Captain Meriwether Lewis called out. "Stop the horses! We need to take a short rest."

The Corps of Discovery, spread out along the difficult terrain of the Rocky Mountains, struggled to make the command heard by all over the battering rain. One by one the men repeated the order up and down the line and helped one another tie their few horses to trees, afraid of losing even one of the valuable animals.

Once all were secured, Sergeant Patrick Gass brushed snow off a cold, hard rock before sitting down. He dug through the well-worn knapsack he'd been carrying since he joined the group almost two years earlier. As he searched for his diary, Patrick marveled at how his life had changed.

Before meeting Captains Meriwether Lewis and William Clark, Patrick had been a carpenter for the army. After hearing about the Corps' plans, he immediately volunteered to join them. Now, here he sat, freezing in the frigid forest air. But the cold wasn't Patrick's biggest problem. He was close to starving, and at times he wondered if he'd survive another day.

Patrick was part of a mission to discover if there was a water route across America. Once the Corps located a northwest passage, the pathway for westward expansion would be set.

Patrick was proud to be part of the journey, and he was one of only seven men documenting the trip through journal entries.

Patrick smiled slightly as he sighted his notebook in a **recess** of his pack. It was hard to write with gloves on, but Patrick didn't dare remove them. If he did, his fingers would freeze like ten icicles in the Rocky Mountain air.

an actual sketch from Patrick Gass's journal

Patrick turned to a clean page and scrawled across the top:

September 14 Thursday 1805

In quick, fluid strokes, Patrick described the situation:

"*Without a miracle it is impossible to feed thirty hungry men and upwards, besides some Indians. So Captain Lewis gave out some portable soup, which he had along, to be used in case of necessity. Some of the men did not **relish** this soup, and—*" Patrick stopped writing when two men sitting next to him deliberately **upset** their soup bowls and jumped up from their seats.

"This soup stinks!" one of the men shouted in a loud, echoing voice.

"Garbage!" the other complained.

"You must eat it. There is no other choice," Captain Clark said and shook his head. "There are no berries to pick or animals to trap up here. This soup, made from cows' hooves, is the only nourishment we have."

Before the men could begin complaining again, an odd clap of thunder sounded. Everyone turned to find it was the thundering of hooves. A couple of powerful packhorses had pulled free and were now bounding downhill at top speed.

"After them!" Captain Lewis shouted, leading the charge. "I don't know how we'll make it over these difficult mountains if we lose those horses."

Many tense minutes later, the escapees were secured, and the men resumed eating the horrid soup.

Sacagawea, the young Native American woman who acted as a translator for Lewis and Clark, stepped toward Patrick. She was carrying a bowl of the soup.

"Here," she said as she handed it to him.

His stomach soured at the smell. This soup was vile. But since there wasn't anything else to eat, he raised the bowl to his chapped, dry lips and took a long drink. Gagging, Patrick forced himself to swallow.

Patrick knew that serving the troops was not part of Sacagawea's responsibilities, but she did it anyway. It was clear that she felt responsible for the men and their well-being.

Sacagawea was an amazing young woman. Not only did she interpret for the group, but she also cared for her infant son, worked as a guide, and helped care for the men as they crossed prairies, forests, and now mountains. Patrick never once heard her complain.

Patrick wished he could be more like Sacagawea, but it was hard—between the never-ending trek, hunger, and cold, he was full of complaints!

"Thank you," he said graciously to Sacagawea, handing her the empty bowl. The little bit of food hadn't been nearly enough for a big man like himself. Patrick was still very, very hungry.

Taking the bowl, Sacagawea nodded before walking back to her husband, Toussaint Charbonneau, a burly French trapper who was tending to the soup pot set over a fire that was almost extinguished by the rain.

With a shiver, Patrick looked down at his journal and reread what he had written. He'd stopped mid-sentence but couldn't recall how he meant to finish. "Oh, bother," he mumbled, closing the journal cover with a snap.

It was time to go anyway. They needed to push forward to find a good place to set up camp for the night. Patrick would finish the entry when they stopped.

As Patrick slipped his knapsack back onto his shoulders, his stomach rumbled.

A few hours until supper. More horrible soup. A little melted snow to drink.

Utterly unsatisfying.

For the hundredth time that day, Patrick wondered if he would survive to see the Pacific Ocean.

By the time Captain Clark called for the Corps to take a **recess** for the night, it was snowing. Patrick,

on duty to unload tents from one of the horses, worked as quickly as he could to remove the burden from the beast.

"*Brrr*," Patrick shivered, setting up the tiny tent he shared with another man. Once set, he slipped inside and wrapped himself in his thin, frayed woolen blanket. He was so cold, so hungry, that when Captain Lewis rang the dinner bell, Patrick could barely move.

"Let's go eat," his tent mate, Private Hugh Hall, said in a rough voice. Hugh had been a soldier in Massachusetts before he joined the Corps.

"I'm too exhausted to move," Patrick told him.

"C'mon. I've heard that we are only a few days from Nez Perce territory." Hugh helped Patrick to his feet. "Certainly the natives will have more filling food for us to eat. Until then, you must keep up your energy."

"My energy is already gone," Patrick said with a groan, losing his balance and falling back down.

Hugh took a long look at his fellow explorer, **upset** about Patrick's condition. "I'll be right back." Hugh disappeared outside the tent, swallowed up by the rapidly falling snowflakes.

Patrick could hear Hugh talking to Captain Lewis. "We must have meat," Hugh was saying in a firm voice. "Without hearty food, men like Patrick Gass will die."

Suddenly, Patrick could hear many voices getting involved in a loud debate just outside.

"If we kill just one, the meat will save many lives," Hugh continued.

"It is a bad idea." Patrick recognized the voice of Private Peter Weiser. "We need every single last one of those horses to carry our supplies!"

Captains Lewis and Clark joined the discussion. There were some men in the Corps fiercely arguing that they needed to eat at least one of the horses tonight in order to survive. Others were disgusted by the idea, saying instead that they needed the living horsepower in order to make it over the mountains.

Then Patrick heard the voice of Sacagawea's husband.

"In France, during the Revolution, many people ate their horses to stay alive."

Sacagawea spoke next. "I value the horses and am grateful to my brother for providing them. We cannot eat them. They are sacred."

"But the men are starving," Hugh countered. "The soup is not enough."

"We will weigh the wisdom of how to proceed," Captain Lewis said with finality. Two sets of footsteps were heard moving away from the crowd, then the air fell silent.

A short time later, Hugh entered the tent where Patrick lay, almost delirious from hunger. Hugh was carrying a bowl full of cooked meat.

The captains had decided that the men's survival depended more on eating well on this night than on having the horse available to carry their belongings in the future.

Knowing his life was at stake, Patrick slathered on a **relish** of dried onions and vinegar and ate every morsel, then fell into a sound sleep.

When Patrick awoke, he was surprised to find that it was still September 14. He lit a tallow candle, opened his journal, and finished his half-written sentence: *"Some of the men did not relish the soup, and agreed to kill a colt; which they immediately did and set about roasting; and which appeared to me to be good eating."*

He then set the journal aside and went back to sleep, resting soundly without hunger pains, for the remainder of the night.

The next morning, Patrick felt good. Healthy. Ready to go on.

As he packed his belongings, Patrick

learned that Captain Lewis had named the place where they camped "Killed Colt Creek." This was in memory of the horse that had given its life to save theirs.

Five days later, the Corps of Discovery made it over the Rocky Mountains and found the Nez Perce, who fed and cared for the group while they made canoes to continue their journey westward.

Analyze the Characters, Setting, and Plot

- Who are the characters in the story?
- Where and when does the story take place?
- What problems do the characters face?
- What does the time period of the story have to do with the characters' problems?
- What solution to the problem do the characters decide upon?

Comprehension:
Text Structure and Organization

- The authors use sequence-of-events text structure to organize this story. Identify two examples of sequence words or phrases.
- Reread the paragraph about Sacagawea on page 11. What text structure do the authors use for this section? How can you tell what text structure is being used?
- On page 10, Captain Clark says, "You must eat it. There is no other choice. There are no berries to pick or animals to trap up here. This soup, made from cows' hooves, is the only nourishment we have." This is an example of cause-and-effect text structure. Explain how.

Focus on Point of View

Point of view means the person's perspective from which a story is told. Writers choose from one of three points of view.
1. First-person point of view uses the main character as the narrator of the story. This type of story is told from the "I" point of view.
2. Second-person point of view uses the understood "you" as the narrator of the story. This point of view is rarely used in narratives.
3. Third-person point of view uses pronouns like **he**, **she**, and **it**. The narrator is not identified in the story.
From which point of view is this story told?

Analyze the Tools Writers Use: Alliteration

- On page 9, the authors write that Patrick is freezing in the frigid forest air. How is this an example of alliteration?

- On page 11, the authors write that Patrick's stomach soured at the smell of the soup. What does this alliterative phrase emphasize?

- On page 12, the authors write that Patrick thinks the soup is utterly unsatisfying. The authors use alliteration with the "uh" sound. How does this emphasize the action?

Focus on Words: Homonyms

Make a chart like the one below. Locate the homonyms in the story. Define each word and identify its part of speech.

Page	Word	Definition	Part of Speech
10	recess		
12	recess		
10	relish		
15	relish		
10	upset		
14	upset		

The title tells readers the historical event on which the story is based.

Building the Transcontinental Railroad:

Blasting Through the Sierra Nevadas

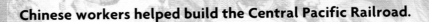

Chinese workers helped build the Central Pacific Railroad.

The authors introduce Chang Han, a main character, and his initial problem: He's physically suffering while trying to do his job. The authors want readers to make a connection to Chang and "feel" his pain. Readers who care about a character are more inclined to keep reading.

Chang Han couldn't feel his toes. They were so cold that they were numb. His fingers weren't much better. It was getting harder and harder to hold the heavy pick he was using to cut through the stone.

"Chang?" It was his friend Wen Lin.

"Yes?" Chang turned to look at Wen, but it was so dark in the tunnel that he couldn't see very far.

The two men had been neighbors in China. They had traveled a long way together, selling small packets of fireworks that Chang had made to pay for ship passage to America.

During the journey, they agreed that when they each had three hundred dollars in their pockets, they would return to China. Wen wanted to buy a small farm for his wife and two sons. Chang planned to move to the city.

Laying train track through mountains was a difficult and slow process in the mid-1800s.

"I am freezing," Wen told Chang, his teeth chattering. "At this pace, we are going to be chopping at the same piece of rock for the rest of our lives."

Chang could hear the scrape of the shovel against the tunnel's floor as Wen lifted into a pushcart the little bits of mountain that Chang shaved off with his pick.

The characters of Chang and Wen are fictional, but they are based on the many Chinese workers who built the railroads. Their dialogue is invented by the authors, but it sounds realistic for the setting and characters.

The story is not based on a specific historical event, but the setting and story line are based on what really happened when the railroad was built. Note that the story is told using the third-person narrator.

It was March 1867. It had been a whole year since Chang and Wen had been hired by the Central Pacific Railroad to work on the Transcontinental Railroad.

The idea was simple: Workers on the West Coast of America would build a train track headed east. From the East, workers would extend the Union Pacific Railroad westward. The two tracks were to meet up in Utah.

And yet, while the idea sounded easy enough, actually building the railroad was very difficult. The track needed to go straight through the mighty Sierra Nevada Mountains.

a train crossing a bridge in 1858

The authors conducted research and included actual historical facts. Including details from history helps readers feel as if they are in the time and place of the story.

For twenty-five dollars a month, the men worked long, hard shifts, carving away inch by inch at the mountainside. Progress was terribly slow. The meeting of the two trains was still a year and a half away, but if they didn't get through Summit Point soon, the entire railroad project would be delayed.

"I wish there was a way to move more quickly," Wen said with a shiver. "I hear there is desert on the other side of this monstrous mountain. At least the desert is warm."

"Not warm. Hot," Chang corrected.

"Warm, hot—as long as it's not cold," Wen said. "Can't you work faster, Chang? I'm tired of snow. I want to smell some sweet sunshine." He sniffed the air, imagining.

Chang laughed. "I'm working as fast as I can." With a grunt, he raised his pick and struck it hard against the stony wall before him, but only a tiny chunk of rock fell to the ground.

The next morning, Chang was startled awake by a huge explosion. The small wooden cabin that Chang shared with his work team shook wildly.

The authors develop the story. They describe an explosion, a major event that occurred during the building of the railroad. They want readers to experience the danger and fear as if they were present.

Chang leapt out of bed. "What's going on?" he asked his team's leader, Hong Li.

"I don't know," Hong replied, slipping into his shoes and coat. "We better go find out."

Chang looked around for Wen. He wasn't in the cabin or just outside. Chang began to worry. He hurried in the direction of the blast.

The Chinese workers' living area was set aside from the **compound** where the rest of the crews lived. The American teams had things better. They were paid ten dollars more a month and they didn't have to buy their own tools, supplies, or food.

For the first time, Chang was glad his cabin was pushed back from the work site. Those who had been close to the tunnel when the explosion happened suffered from the impact. Chang called Wen's name as he rushed past huts that had been crushed by an avalanche of snow.

"Wen!" Chang called. "Where are you?" With each step, his concern grew. "Wen!" Chang called as he went to **peer** into the dust that was floating around the tunnel, like a thick, gray cloud.

"Chang!" his friend finally replied. "Come quick. We need your help."

Chang hurried to the mouth of the Summit Tunnel. There stood Wen, shoulder to shoulder with railroad workers from England, Ireland, and America. They were using picks and shovels to dig out three men who'd been trapped inside the tunnel by the blast.

His gloves and pick were still back in the hut, so Chang used his bare hands to pull aside large chunks of rocks, hoping that the men inside were still alive.

"Whew," Wen sighed as he finally sat down to rest after the three men were rescued. "Those men are very lucky."

"Do you know what happened?" Chang asked.

Wen usually knew what was going on because, even though they'd been in America the same amount of time, his English was better than Chang's. "Just before the explosion, I overheard two Americans talking. They said that there is a new man named James Howden in the British camp."

The name was unfamiliar to Chang.

Wen continued, "James Howden is an engineer. He told the workers that instead of cutting through the mountain with a pick and shovel, he will show them how to use a **compound** of chemicals to blast through the rock."

The authors advance the plot with dialogue that tells readers about James Howden and his new explosive. Howden was an actual explosives expert who worked on the railroad.

"Aah," Chang said. "That explains the explosion."

"Mr. Howden told everyone that he could control the blast." Wen glanced at all the bits of rock that were scattered around.

"Well, he was wrong," Chang replied.

Wen sighed, his cold breath brittle in the frigid air.

James Howden was a Scottish engineer who helped build the Transcontinental Railroad.

"I wish the explosives had worked. Blasting would be much better than digging," Wen said.

"Workers! Workers!" Hong Li's voice echoed through the trees. "It is time for our shift to begin."

Chang hurried back to the hut to gather his supplies. When he returned, Mr. Howden was speaking to the Chinese crew, holding a small crate. "Who will take this new explosive into the tunnel?"

No one volunteered.

The authors introduce a new conflict: Someone has to take the explosives into the tunnel.

"No need to fear the nitroglycerin. I know what went wrong," Mr. Howden said, understanding the situation. He held up the crate higher. "I made a better fuse this time."

"Nitroglycerin?" A man near Chang backed away from Mr. Howden. "You do not want to touch that!" he told those around him. "My sister's husband wrote about it in a letter. In San Francisco, a crate exploded and fifteen people died."

"Nitroglycerin," Chang repeated the name of the substance softly to himself. Even though he had been a master fireworks maker, working with explosives his whole life in China, he'd never heard of it. Fireworks were made of gunpowder and salts. Sure, they could be dangerous, but not if they were handled properly.

"We do not want to use the explosives," Hong told Mr. Howden.

"Without blasting, we will never finish the railroad in time." Mr. Howden was growing frustrated.

Hong looked out at his team. "Will anyone take the crate into the tunnel?" Again, no one raised his hand.

Mr. Howden offered the men extra money. He said he'd get them supplies, more food, new clothes, but all the men stepped back, refusing the task.

"If no one volunteers, I will be forced to choose someone," Mr. Howden said, looking over the faces of the workers. His eyes settled on Wen. "You." He pointed at Wen Lin. "I saw how fast and hard you worked to help save those other men. You will be able to place the crate, then run out in time." Mr. Howden tried to hand the crate to Wen.

The authors established Chang's expertise with explosives in the beginning of the story. Now that expertise will become part of the story. But how? Readers know that Chang is a "good guy," so they'll worry about him—and keep reading.

"No. Please," Wen said, "I do not want to die! Not me. Please."

Mr. Howden stood firm. The construction of the Transcontinental Railroad was on a timetable and it was already behind schedule.

Wen turned quickly to Chang. "You know about explosives. I am certain you can save my life."

> The authors describe a new conflict for Chang: Does he step forward to save his friend? How will he stay safe if he takes Wen's place?

Chang had an idea of how to make the nitroglycerin blast safer, but he wasn't sure it would work. "Fireworks are very different," he told Wen.

Wen's eyes were full of hope. "You must try."

Chang agreed to speak to Mr. Howden. "If we wrap the nitroglycerin in a paper tube, like we do with fireworks in China, and add a long fuse, the worker who sets the blast will have much more time to run before the chemicals explode."

For a long moment, Mr. Howden stared at Chang.

"I see your point," Mr. Howden said at last, listening to the Chinese man as he would a **peer**. "Let's try it."

This photograph was taken at Promontory Point, Utah, at the historic meeting of the two railroad construction crews.

Chang was so nervous that his knees were knocking. Since he'd created the paper tube, he wanted to be the one to take it into the tunnel.

Very carefully, Chang placed the tube in the farthest rock wall, lit the fuse, and then ran as fast as he could.

Boom!

The explosion pushed Chang the last few feet out of the tunnel. He flew face first into the freezing snow.

"It worked!" Chang said as the men around him cheered. Inside the tunnel, rock debris safely crumbled down.

"Thank you, Chang! We are a few feet closer to the desert already!" Wen said, putting an arm around his friend.

"I know," Chang said, sniffing the air, "I can almost smell the sunshine."

The story ends with a successful solution to the problem. Chang, a lowly worker, is the hero. The authors are using historical fiction to make a comment about fairness and equality that has meaning for today's readers.

Analyze the Characters, Setting, and Plot

- Who are the characters in the story?
- Where and when does the story take place?
- What problem do the characters face?
- How do the characters solve the problem?
- Which characters play a big role in the solution to the problem?

Comprehension:
Text Structure and Organization

- The authors use sequence-of-events text structure to organize this story. Identify two examples of sequence words or phrases.
- On page 22, the authors contrast American and Chinese workers. Identify the sentence that tells you the authors are contrasting.
- What cause-and-effect clue word do the authors use in showing that Wen's English was better than Chang's English?

Analyze the Tools Writers Use: Alliteration

- On page 21, Wen uses the words "monstrous mountain." How is this an example of alliteration?
- On page 21, Wen says, "I want to smell some sweet sunshine." What does this alliterative phrase emphasize?
- On page 22, the authors write that "Chang called Wen's name as he rushed past huts that had been crushed by an avalanche of snow." The authors use assonance with the "uh" sound. How does this emphasize the action?

Focus on Words: Homonyms

Make a chart like the one below. Locate the homonyms in the story. Define each word and identify its part of speech.

Page	Word	Definition	Part of Speech
22	compound		
23	compound		
22	peer		
27	peer		

Chinese American railroad laborers often did the most difficult jobs.

How does an author write HISTORICAL FICTION?

Reread "Building the Transcontinental Railroad" and think about what Stacia Deutsch and Rhody Cohon did to write this story. How did they develop the story? How can you, as a writer, develop your own historical fiction?

1. Decide on a Time and Place in History

a. Choose a time 30 years ago, 3,000 years ago, or somewhere in between. Set your story in your home country or far away.

b. Learn everything you can about the lives of people who lived in that time and place so your story details will be authentic. In "Building the Transcontinental Railroad," the author researched how Chinese immigrants working on the Transcontinental Railroad lived and worked.

c. Choose an actual event as the background for your own historical fiction story, or create a story based on the life of a historical figure.

Character	Chang Han	Wen Lin
Traits	hard working; loyal friend; problem solver	loyal family man; afraid of being in danger
Examples	Chang Han has worked at the tough job of chipping away at the rock of the Sierra Nevada Mountains for a year; he saves his friend, Wen Lin, from having to place the nitroglycerin in the tunnel and comes up with the idea of putting a long fuse on the explosives to make it safer for the workers	Wen Lin has traveled halfway across the world from his home in China to do the grueling work of building the railroad in America in order to earn enough money to buy a farm for his wife and sons back home; he is afraid to place the nitroglycerin in the cave when he is chosen to do so and appeals to his friend, Chang Han, to help him

Brainstorm Characters

Writers ask these questions:

- What kind of person will my main character be?
  What are his or her traits, or qualities?
- What things are important to my main character?
  What does he or she want?
- What other characters will be important to my story?
  How will each character help or hinder the main character?
- How will the characters change? What will they learn about life?

Brainstorm Plot

Writers ask these questions:

- What are some important incidents that actually occurred
  in my historical setting? How can I turn one of those real-life
  events into a story?
- What is the problem, or situation?
- What events happen?
- How does the story end?
- Will my readers be entertained? Will they learn something?

Setting	the Sierra Nevada Mountains, 1867
Problem of the Story	It is very slow, difficult work trying to dig a tunnel through the Sierras for the railroad—and there is a deadline.
Story Events	1. Workers, including Chang Han and Wen Lin, have been slowing chipping away at the rock of the Sierra Nevada Mountains to make a tunnel for a Transcontinental Railroad, and it's freezing cold inside the mountain. 2. One day there is a big explosion and three men are trapped inside the tunnel. 3. Chang and Wen help dig out the men, who are lucky to be alive. 4. They discover that an engineer, James Howden, has a powerful new explosive—nitroglycerin—that can make the job go quickly but has caused this frightening explosion.
Solution to the Problem	Chang Han not only spares his friend from a dangerous mission by volunteering himself, but he also figures out how to make handling the explosives safe: He devises a long fuse so that the handler has time to get safely away.

Glossary

compound   (KAHM-pownd) *noun* an area containing a group of buildings and homes (page 22)

compound   (KAHM-pownd) *noun* a substance made with a mixture of different parts (page 23)

peer   (PEER) *verb* look (page 22)

peer   (PEER) *noun* person of equal standing (page 27)

recess   (REE-ses) *noun* secret part (page 10)

recess   (REE-ses) *verb* to take a break in doing something (page 12)

relish   (REH-lish) *verb* like; enjoy (page 10)

relish   (REH-lish) *noun* a condiment added to food to add flavor (page 15)

upset   (up-SET) *verb* to overturn (page 10)

upset   (up-SET) *adjective* disturbed; distraught (page 14)